GUIDES

ELECTRICIAN

REAL LIFE GUIDES

Practical guides for practical people

In this increasingly sophisticated world the need for manually skilled people to build our homes, cut our hair, fix our boilers, and make our cars go is greater than ever. As things progress, so the level of training and competence required of our skilled manual workers increases.

In this new series of career guides from Trotman, we look in detail at what it takes to train for, get into, and be successful at a wide spectrum of practical careers. *Real Life Guides* aim to inform and inspire young people and adults alike by providing comprehensive yet hard-hitting and often blunt information about what it takes to succeed in these careers.

The other titles in the series are:

Real Life Guide: the Armed Forces

Real Life Guide: the Beauty Industry

Real Life Guide: Carpentry & Cabinet-Making

Real Life Guide: Catering

Real Life Guide: Construction

Real Life Guide: Hairdressing

Real Life Guide: the Motor Industry

Real Life Guide: Plumbing

Real Life Guide: Retailing

Real Life Guide: Working Outdoors

trotman

ELECTRICIAN

Roger Jones

Real Life Guide: Electrician
This first edition published in 2004 by Trotman and Company Ltd
2 The Green, Richmond, Surrey TW9 1PL

The material in this book was correct at time of going to press.
Unfortunately information can quickly go out of date and readers
are urged to check on the latest details with the appropriate
authorities before entering into any agreements.

Editorial and Publishing Team
Author Roger Jones
Editorial Rachel Lockhart, Commissioning Editor;
Anya Wilson, Editor; Bianca Knights, Assistant Editor
Production Ken Ruskin, Head of Pre-press and Production
Sales and Marketing Deborah Jones, Head of Sales and
Marketing

Trotman Publishing Board
Managing Director Toby Trotman
Commercial Director Tom Lee
Editorial Director Mina Patria

British Library Cataloguing in Publication Data
A catalogue record for this book is available from the British Library

ISBN 0 85660 998 6

Typeset by Photoprint, Torquay
Printed and bound in Great Britain by Cromwell Press, Trowbridge,
Wiltshire

Real Life

GUIDES

CONTENTS

Acknowledgements

I should like to thank a number of people and organisations for the help and advice they have given me in the preparation of this book, notably Tony Morgan, Malcolm Holmes of GLOSCAT, Jon Dicken and Lindsey Palser of Clarkson Evans, Tom Croose, Leon Newman, Ben Pillinger, James Purveur, John Sowler, Philip Trewin, EESTC, Energy & Utility Skills, Energy Networks Association, ETT, JTL, National Grid Transco, SECTT and Summit Skills.

Roger Jones

About the author

Roger Jones is a freelance writer who has written extensively on careers topics, education and living and working abroad. His other books include *You Want to Work WHERE?!*, published by Trotman, *Getting a Job Abroad*, *Getting a Job in America* and *Culture Smart! Thailand*.

Introduction

What is the first thing you do in the morning? Switch on the light? Turn on the radio? Have a bath? Boil a kettle? Take the milk out of the fridge? Make yourself some toast? Look at the latest emails on your computer?

Can you spot what all these have in common? They all use electricity, of course.

Electricity plays a vital part in our daily lives, but we tend to take it for granted. How could we possibly manage without it? It hardly bears thinking about. There would be no lights that you can switch on and off, no TV or radio, no computers or ATMs, no tube trains, no washing machines or dishwashers, no microwave ovens or electric cookers.

> Electricity plays a vital part in our daily lives, but we tend to take it for granted.

Where you have electricity you need to have people with electrical skills. Most of us know how to fit a plug or change a light bulb, but very few people know what to do when the washing machine breaks down or there is a power blackout. In circumstances like these you send for an electrician.

You are doubtless familiar with the service engineers who come to repair appliances in the home or office – the people who get the electric cooker or washing machine working again when it conks out or who coax the photocopier back into life. But these electricians are just the tip of the iceberg.

Working behind the scenes there are others you rarely, if ever, see. These are the people who generate the electricity, who distribute it to our homes and workplaces, who wire up houses, offices, factories and public buildings and ensure the electrical systems are safe, who manufacture a whole range of electrical and electronic goods for which the modern consumer has an insatiable appetite.

Just take a look at the following list of jobs and decide which of them require electrical skills and knowledge.

- Aerospace technician
- Assembly worker/operative
- Broadcasting engineer
- Deck officer (Navy or Merchant Navy)
- Engineering technician
- Lighting or sound technician
- Maintenance technician
- Military technician
- Railway fitter or linesperson
- Security alarm fitter
- Service engineer
- Signalling technician
- Telecommunications technician
- Vehicle mechanic

All of them do – to a greater or lesser extent.

AEROSPACE TECHNICIAN
The Montgolfier brothers, who pioneered hot-air balloon travel, may have managed to get into the air without

electricity, but all modern aeroplanes have a huge amount of sophisticated electrical equipment aboard. Technicians with electrical and electronic expertise are employed at the production stage to install electronic systems, such as automatic landing systems, and by airlines to maintain the aircraft at peak effectiveness.

ASSEMBLY WORKER/OPERATIVE
Manufacturing is in decline in the UK, but companies making electrical goods or electronic components seem to be making a comeback. Companies need well-trained technicians capable of making high-value goods, such as computers, electronic circuits, measuring equipment, control systems and telecommunications equipment.

BROADCASTING ENGINEER
When you switch on the TV you see and hear only the performers, but behind every TV or radio programme there are others working in the background. They include engineers who install, maintain and repair equipment used in broadcasting studios and at transmitting stations, and also the landlines and radio link circuits.

DECK OFFICER (NAVY OR MERCHANT NAVY)
Deck officers use a lot of sophisticated electronic equipment for navigation, steering and other ship's operations, and need to be able to repair it or service it in co-operation with the ship's engineers. Don't forget that large liners often have the electricity-generating capacity of a town.

ENGINEERING TECHNICIAN
Electrical/Electronic engineering technicians are involved in a number of industries from manufacturing power-generating

equipment to the development and testing of circuits and electronic components.

LIGHTING OR SOUND TECHNICIAN

Providing lighting and sound in a theatre or hall, or for an outside event, requires people with a sound knowledge of electricity as well as artistic flair. You don't want the lights to go out in the middle of a pop concert, do you? You will find out more about this in the Trotman guide dealing with the media, *Media Uncovered*.

MAINTENANCE TECHNICIAN

Large factories and public authorities usually have electricians on their permanent payroll to carry out maintenance on their electrical fixtures and equipment.

MILITARY TECHNICIAN

The armed forces train and employ people to install and maintain electrical facilities, and to look after the generation and distribution of power in temporary and permanent camps. Electronics technicians in the armed services maintain and repair electronic systems, including guided weapons systems and communications. Royal Signals electricians are responsible for communications systems.

RAILWAY FITTER OR LINESPERSON

London Underground and Network Rail are two of the larger organisations that employ skilled personnel to install, renew and maintain the electrical rails and overhead line equipment which power electric trains, as well as the power systems of the trains themselves.

SECURITY ALARM FITTER

This work involves laying electrical cables, connecting equipment to the mains, testing it and maintaining it. In large public and industrial complexes the systems can be extremely complex.

SERVICE ENGINEER

Service engineers are responsible for installing, maintaining and repairing electrical equipment in homes, offices and factories. This equipment includes washing machines, photocopiers, air-conditioning, television sets, etc.

SIGNALLING TECHNICIAN

In the past the signalling systems that controlled the movement of trains were mechanical. Nowadays they are operated by electricity. People are employed to construct and fit new signalling equipment, check and adjust the equipment in place and repair faults.

TELECOMMUNICATIONS TECHNICIAN

Telecommunications are very sophisticated these days and a wide range of skills are needed for installing and servicing telecommunications networks, running wires and cables from exchanges to homes, offices and factories, maintaining satellite and mobile links.

VEHICLE MECHANIC

Most modern vehicles have an array of electrical and electronic equipment, including electronic ignition systems, computerised dashboards, burglar alarms, etc. Larger garages employ auto-electricians for fault-finding, testing and repairing electrical components.

This is only a selection of the jobs in which electrical skills play a role. If you type in the word 'electrician' on the Worktrain website (www.worktrain.gov.uk) you will come across at least another dozen jobs in which electrical skills are important. Most of them are interesting jobs that command respect and are open to anybody with the right attitude and aptitude. Anyone with an electrical qualification can count on having a job for life and the opportunity to progress to positions of responsibility that pay well. Read on and you'll get a flavour of what the job is like and decide whether it appeals enough for you to want to take things further.

ELECTRICITY MILESTONES

600BC: Thales of Miletus produces static electricity by rubbing a piece of amber.

1752:   Benjamin Franklin invents the lightning conductor.

1831:   Michael Faraday discovers how electricity can be generated.

1879:   Thomas Edison begins manufacturing light filaments.

1890:   The world's first electric underground railway, the City and South London, opens.

1920s: Appliances like electric heaters, kettles and fridges appear in people's homes.

1938:   Two-thirds of homes in the UK are supplied with electricity.

1956:   Britain's first nuclear power station opens at Calder Hall.

TONY MORGAN
Success story

1

When Tony Morgan joined the Southern
Electricity Board as an apprentice at the
age of 15, little did he expect that one day
he would become chairman of a company
with 270 employees and President of the
prestigious Electrical Contractors'
Association.

'I had no idea what I would do when I left
school, but my elder brother suggested
that a career in the electrical industry
would be good for me, so I dutifully took
his advice. I was up against strong
competition at the interview, but I think the
selectors saw I had vocational skills, rather
than academic ability, and good personal
skills as well, so they decided to offer me
an apprenticeship.'

Back in the 1950s an apprenticeship was
for a fixed period of six years and Tony did
not emerge as a fully-fledged electrician
until he was 21. It was a 'well-rounded'
apprenticeship: in addition to learning all
aspects of the electrician's craft, such as
motor repairs, installations and fault-
finding, he also gained experience in the
office, learning how the system worked
and how customers were dealt with. The

You have to
be passionate
about what
you want to
do, whether
as a
craftsman or
a business
person.

apprenticeship included one day a week studying at Salisbury College, which he looks back on with gratitude.

'I was always carefully supervised at work,' he recalls. 'It was not until the last six to nine months of my apprenticeship that I was allowed to rewire a house by myself, and that was under supervision. We had a more cautious approach then. That was because safety devices were not as sophisticated as they have now become.'

But after a while he became disillusioned with working in what was then a large nationalised industry.

'I was very proud of my skills and ability, and although I was working with some excellent people, one got very few pats on the back from management and I felt I was not properly appreciated. So at the age of 23 I decided to set up on my own as a self-employed electrician.'

A friend offered to join him as an electrician's mate, and one of their first contracts was wiring the pumps of a filling station – a job that needed special skills and knowledge. The two of them attracted a good range of work, wiring new houses and replacing lead cabling, which was then reaching the end of its life. A couple of years later he took on an apprentice. Two years after that he formed a partnership with another electrical craftsman, and the firm Wessex Electrical Contractors was born.

The 1970s saw steady growth and Wessex developed close relationships with a local building firm that was going from strength to strength, and an expanding food manufacturer. 'We had no formal agreements; we operated on the basis of trust,' Tony notes. As the company expanded he found he had to leave the electrical work to others while he concentrated on the business side of the operation.

Nowadays the firm consists of four trading companies, with a total turnover of over £16 million, that specialise in: electrical contracting; building services; commercial catering engineering services; and fire and security. The fire and security firm recently installed fire detection systems at the massive new GCHQ building in Cheltenham, the Government's spy base.

Tony's sons now deal with the day-to-day running of the business together with the four management boards. Since becoming ECA President at the beginning of May 2004, Tony devotes much of his energy to the activities of the Association. Now that disparate technologies are beginning to converge, he is especially keen to collaborate with other specialist engineering sectors.

Nowadays the firm consists of four trading companies, with a total turnover of over £16 million, that specialise in: electrical contracting; building services; commercial catering engineering services; and fire and security.

What advice does he have for anyone who is starting out in the electrical industries?

'You have to be passionate about what you want to do, whether as a craftsman or a business person. If you eventually want to strike out on your own, as I did, there is a wealth of good advice available out there. But you should never go into business unless you are keen to succeed.'

While not everybody will necessarily want to take the self-employment route, Tony Morgan's success shows that the sky really is the limit for anyone planning a career in electrical engineering.

2

What's the story?

This book looks at a wide range of jobs in which the title 'electrician' is used. We have already seen that there is a range of different titles for people with electrical skills. All electricians require more or less the same basic knowledge and skills, but their actual day-to-day tasks vary according to the type of work in which they are involved. These tasks include some – though by no means all – of the following.

- Installing and maintaining all the cables, conduits, fitments, meters, switchgear, wiring and other equipment needed for the efficient and safe use of electricity.
- Using various hand tools and power tools to measure, cut, join and fit cabling, wiring and equipment.
- Working from plans and technical drawings to run cabling and to place lights, sockets and switches.
- Testing installations to ensure they are effective and completely safe.
- Installing the wiring and electrical components in complex electrical and electronic equipment.
- Diagnosing, locating and repairing faults in installations and electrical equipment.
- Designing and developing new electrical and electronic appliances and systems.

This may sound like a very tall order, but in fact electricians tend to specialise in one particular area. The main ones are:

- Electricity supply and distribution – producing electricity at power stations and supplying it to the consumer. This is the first stage of the electrical process: from the power station to the meter.
- Electrical contracting – installing and maintaining electrical systems for heating, lighting, ventilation, refrigeration, lifts, etc. This is the second stage of the electrical process: from the meter to the plug.
- Electrical and electronics manufacture – making, fitting and testing the electrical parts of machines and appliances, as well as developing new ones. This is the final stage of the electrical process: the appliances you plug into the electrical supply.
- Electrical and electronics servicing – maintaining and repairing machines and appliances that use electricity.

ELECTRICITY SUPPLY AND DISTRIBUTION

Electricity is generated at power stations (which may be nuclear, coal-fired or gas-fired), wind farms and hydro-electric plants and then transmitted at high voltages from power stations by overhead or underground cables – a sort of electrical motorway.

DID YOU KNOW?

The National Grid has 7,000 kilometres of overhead lines, 600 kilometres of underground cables and some 300 substations which control the voltage and distribution of electricity. Electricity is generated at about 25,000 volts but is transmitted around the grid system at 275,000 and 400,000 volts. The voltage is reduced to 132,000 when it is passed on to regional distribution networks, and these reduce it again to 11,000 volts at their substations. Local substations reduce it further to 230 volts.

In England and Wales the distribution system is owned and operated by the National Grid Company. Scotland has two companies operating its transmission network (Scottish Power, and Scottish and Southern Energy), while Northern Ireland is served by Northern Ireland Electricity. The network links the power stations and allows large amounts of electricity to be transmitted around the country to meet demand.

Local distribution companies in England and Wales take electricity from the grid and carry it to towns, villages and smaller industrial customers using local wires, transformers, substations. They are CE Electric in the North; Central Networks in the Midlands; EDF Energy in London, the East and South East; and Western Power Distribution in the South West and South and West Wales.

Electricity distribution workers install and maintain electricity generation systems which supply homes, businesses and industry and ensure that the electricity supply equipment and machinery is safe and in good working order. The work involves reading and interpreting technical drawings, liaising with engineers, taking instructions and reporting back. They work in a variety of environments, including trenches in the ground where cables are laid, and on electricity pylons. Among the specialist trades are those of:

- Electrical fitter – installs generating equipment, control gear and other plant and machinery.
- Cable jointer – installs power cables underground and connects them properly to overhead supply lines or other parts of the generating system.
- Linesperson – constructs overhead electricity distribution lines and ensures they are properly maintained.

energy networks

distribution network

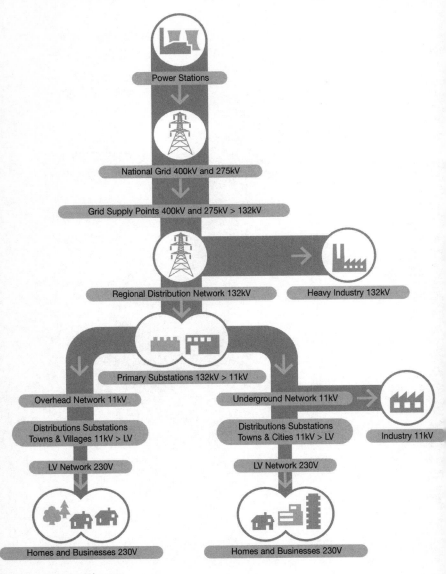

www.energynetworks.org

- Restoration craftsperson – is skilled in all three areas and does repairs to the system in the event of a breakdown.

Working conditions can vary, and technicians have to be prepared to work out of doors in all weathers. Hours can be irregular, especially when electrical breakdowns occur as a result of bad weather or electrical faults in the system. The main employers have been mentioned above, but sometimes contracting firms are used.

Over 100,000 people work in the electrical supply and distribution industry, and the main trade bodies are the Association of Electricity Producers and the Energy Networks Association. The Sector Skills Association which sets standards for the industry and has become responsible for training is Energy & Utility Skills Ltd.

SPECIMEN JOB OUTLINE

Craftsperson, Engineering Services (Substations), National Grid

Qualifications required:

- Apprenticeship or equivalent, including City and Guilds 232 and relevant NVQs
- Full driving licence
- HGV licence (optional)

Experience required:

- Ability to work unsupervised on a wide range of transmission equipment as part of a fully integrated team, but with occasional lone working.
- Must demonstrate a self-help approach to common work-related problems, using IT systems to resolve them.

Job purpose:

- To undertake a range of duties on plant and equipment to defined standards including maintenance, assisting with commissioning, basic fault finding and repair within sphere of competence, and safety implementation.

Job dimensions:

Working as an integral member of a mobile workforce in groups that best match the planned programme of work, travelling direct to and from the point of work, the post holder will work within all functions of the Engineering Services Substations Group as required and will also be required to adopt a flexible approach to work and its completion so as to minimise risk.

Key Tasks:

- To undertake craft duties on a wide range of plant and equipment including fault investigation, repair and routine inspections.

- To carry out the roles of 'authorised person', 'appointed person – cranes', and 'competent person' nominations as per national safety regulations.
- To carry out the roles of 'general safety supervisor' and preferably also 'senior authorised person' within their sphere of operation.
- To perform stand-by duties as per an agreed rota, as appropriate.
- To be pro-active in all aspects of the work programme, communicating with the line manager as appropriate to enable the work programme to be kept on track and updated to maintain target prioritisation as necessary.
- To strive to eliminate all accidents and near misses within the work environment by adopting risk assessment techniques and being aware of potential hazards.
- To provide training to less experienced members of staff.

ELECTRICAL CONTRACTING

If you need to replace wiring in your house or install smoke or fire alarms you will need to call in an electrical contractor. If you are building an airport you will also need an electrical contractor. The first is on a much smaller scale than the second, but similar skills are needed for both.

In essence, electrical contractors design and install the electrical engineering services needed in homes, schools, hospitals, factories, industrial plant and commercial premises. The installations can be traditional power and lighting outlets; or high-tech control, security and data communications systems for automated offices, industrial and environment services. Some projects, like wiring a house, can take a day and be done by just one person; others involve a team of workers and can last years, as was the case with the Channel Tunnel and Canary Wharf.

The Electrical Contractors' Association (ECA) has over 2,000 member companies ranging from small local companies to regional companies (such as Clarkson Evans, which specialises in housing developments in the Midlands) to multinationals such as Balfour Kilpatrick, which has projects all over the world. ECA members employ over 30,000 people and support 8,000 apprentices. Their collective annual turnover is £4.5 billion.

The work can be very diverse. It can include:

- installing electrical wiring, equipment, apparatus and fixtures
- maintaining, repairing and replacing wiring and equipment in older premises
- fixing and connecting the components of electrical installations
- making parts, using hand tools
- testing electrical systems and circuits
- diagnosing and rectifying faults in wiring, apparatus and components
- inspecting electrical systems and parts
- preparing the work site for electrical installation to begin
- restoring the work site when the work has been completed

- identifying and complying with regulatory and statutory requirements.

This is definitely not a nine-to-five job, and early starts tend to be the norm. You may well have to work inside unfinished premises without heating and even outside in the open air. The job involves stretching, bending, lifting, and possibly working in cramped and dusty conditions. Some projects may require you to live away from home for short periods. You may even be posted abroad. However, you will normally receive an accommodation allowance if this happens. The construction sector is currently enjoying a boom, so employment prospects are very good.

This is definitely not a nine-to-five job, and early starts tend to be the norm.

The ECA has joined forces with Amicus-AEEU to form the Joint Industry Board (JIB), which registers apprentices. JIB works closely with JT Ltd (JTL), which is the principal training organiser to the industry in England and Wales. JTL arranges and manages training and funding for apprentices, and also monitors their training and progress. The Scottish equivalent of JIB is SJIB. The main training provider is the Scottish Electrical Charitable Training Trust (SECTT).

ELECTRICAL AND ELECTRONICS MANUFACTURE

This involves making both the goods and appliances that use electricity, and the components used by the electrical supply and distribution companies and by electrical contractors. Around 450,000 people are employed by the

350 companies of the British Electrotechnical and Allied Manufacturers' Association (BEAMA) and they have a turnover of some £65 billion. A further 1.1 million people are employed by members of the Information Technology, Telecommunications and Electronics Association, Intellect, though not all of these will be engaged in manufacture.

The industry manufactures a wide range of equipment, from printed circuit boards, semiconductors and electromechanical components to fully finished articles, such as mobile phones, computers and office machines. The various sectors, in descending order of value, are:

- test measurement and navigation
- computers
- telecommunications
- components
- radio, TV and audio
- office machines.

Assembling electronic and electrical equipment can be intricate work. Assemblers may have to insert electrical components or solder parts on to a circuit board using various hand tools. In some cases you may be merely adding a few parts to an article as it comes by on the assembly line. Not much training is required for this, but these days robots are often used for repetitive tasks, and staff are involved in inspecting and testing finished products.

Assembly work is the most visible part of manufacturing. However, a lot of work goes on behind the scenes: planning, designing, testing and developing new products, and improving old ones. This is where electronic engineering technicians come into their own. Normally, technicians work under the supervision of chartered engineers; they may have to conduct tests to see whether a particular idea for a product is feasible and to assess its reliability. This is responsible work and there is a strong demand for well-trained technicians, notably in the growing IT and telecommunications equipment industries.

Electronics factories are normally well lit, dust-free and very clean. Specialist clothing is often worn, such as overalls, head covering, gloves and safety glasses. Shift work is sometimes worked and part-time work may be available on the production line. Electronics technicians, on the other hand, are more likely to have a nine-to-five job, often work in laboratories or offices rather than on the factory floor and are generally educated to a higher standard. Sometimes travel to different locations will be required to test new equipment.

ELECTRICAL AND ELECTRONICS SERVICING

This a large and diverse sector covering domestic consumer electronics and electrical appliances (such as TVs and washing machines), to commercial equipment, such as photocopiers and industrial machinery. As a result of technological advances and the growth in consumer electronics there is a growing demand for skilled employees within the servicing industry at craft and technical levels.

Domestic electronics/electrical servicing is normally divided into two areas:

● consumer electronics, which covers televisions, radios, hi-fis, video recorders, computers, DVD players and other types of electronic equipment used in the home. Personnel service products either in a customer's home or in a specialist workshop.

- domestic electrical appliances, including washing machines, dishwashers, microwave ovens, cookers and refrigerators. Since these are less portable than TVs and other electronics equipment, domestic appliance engineers tend to repair and service equipment on a customer's premises.

Industrial servicing can cover a variety of tasks. It can involve fixing office equipment, such as computers, photocopiers and fax machines, and making regular maintenance checks. In some cases the work may be more specialised: maintaining complex hospital equipment, air-conditioning systems or electronic equipment in the leisure sector.

Jobs are available with servicing companies, high street chains (such as Comet and PC World) and independent retailers, but a large number of service engineers opt for self-employment once they are fully qualified. Since you will be dealing with members of the general public who may not be technologically aware it is important to be able to communicate effectively and have a pleasant manner.

The Electrical and Electronics Servicing Training Council sets standards for this sector of the electrical industry. It has links with the Institution of Incorporated Engineers and has developed an examination scheme in collaboration with City & Guilds. The entrance qualification for the industry is the Level 2 NVQ or Progression Award in Electrical and Electronics Servicing.

Tools of the trade

3

By this stage you may have decided you really want to be an electrician. Being keen about something is a good sign, but it won't take you all the way. Before a company or training organisation will consider you, it has to be convinced of your suitability for this kind of work. You will probably be asked to take an aptitude test.

You also need to be sure that the electrician's life is right for you. So start off by looking at the following statements and decide which of them apply to you and which don't.

1. I'm in good physical shape.

2. I'm practical and like making things.

3. I'm hopeless at maths and hate studying.

4. I'm a stickler for punctuality and safety.

5. I want a nine-to-five job with no travel.

6. I enjoy the challenge of solving problems.

7. I get confused by written instructions and diagrams.

8. I don't get on well with strangers.

9. My eyesight is atrocious and I can't stand heights.

10. I love playing about with computers.

11. I'm no good at making decisions.

12. I'm not male or white, and I have no useful contacts.

Now check your answers and see how you did.

1. I'm in good physical shape.
Fine. You'll need to be, especially if you are looking for a job in electrical contracting or distribution. You will need to stretch and bend a lot, there may be some climbing to do, and you may need to carry heavy equipment around. This is likely to be less of a concern if you are involved in manufacturing, for example.

2. I'm practical and like making things.
Good. Electricians need to be highly practical and have good manual dexterity and co-ordination. They also need to be able to deal with a wide range of practical tasks.

3. I'm hopeless at maths and hate studying.
Hard luck. Electricians, particularly as they progress in their careers, have to be capable of doing complex calculations – often in their heads. A GCSE in maths and at least two other subjects is usually required to get on an apprenticeship. As regards studying, you will need to spend time at college if you want to progress in your career.

4. I'm a stickler for punctuality and safety.
Excellent. People in the business don't like to be kept

waiting about. You need to be very safety conscious when dealing with electricity, which can be lethal. This means paying close attention to health and safety regulations.

5. I want a nine-to-five job with no travel.
Tough. There aren't many electrical jobs that offer such luxuries. Some electricians have to work on projects away from home or be prepared for call-outs at any time of the day or night. Even if you are working in a factory you may be required to work shifts.

6. I enjoy the challenge of solving problems.
Good. An electrician has to solve problems all the time, such as how to fit things into a confined space, or the best way to fix equipment which has gone wrong.

7. I get confused by written instructions and diagrams.
Oh dear! This does not sound good. Electricians have to be able to understand and follow written instructions and all kinds of diagrams. Wiring things incorrectly can have fatal consequences.

8. I don't get on well with strangers.
That could be a problem. Most electrical jobs bring you in contact with people you don't know, whether as customers or people from other disciplines who are working alongside you. Electricians seldom work in isolation.

9. My eyesight is atrocious and I can't stand heights.
Sadly, you are unlikely to be accepted for training. Most electrical jobs require good eyesight and normal colour vision. While many electrical manufacturing jobs are on the

ground there are a good many other electrical jobs that involve climbing ladders.

10. I love playing about with computers.
Good. A knowledge of IT is a big bonus for electricians. The ability to use computers and electronic measuring instruments is essential in most electrical jobs, and you may need to search databases for information.

11. I'm no good at making decisions.
Another minus point. You'll often find yourself in situations where you have to think on your feet. Electricians have to make quick decisions – and they have to be the right decisions.

12. I'm not male or white, and I have no useful contacts.
It doesn't matter. You'll find people of all races, creeds and colours working in the electrical field, and if you do your job well you'll gain a lot of respect. There's good news for women, too. The electrical industries have long ceased to be exclusively male. This is an industry where skills count for more than background.

To sum up, to become an electrician you need to have the following attributes.

- interest in technology
- manual dexterity
- willingness to learn
- good health
- punctuality
- accuracy
- an awareness of health and safety

- normal eyesight
- adaptability
- a methodical approach

You will also need to have some 'core skills', which all jobs require to a greater or lesser extent. These are:

- Communication. Using speaking and listening skills when discussing work matters with fellow workers and supervisors; following written and spoken instructions carefully and accurately; writing clear reports; and giving clear explanations to people who may not have electrical expertise.
- Information technology. You need to be able to select and use information from computer databases to help diagnose faults, for stock control, keeping records, etc.; and you should also be able to use email and surf the Internet.
- Numeracy. Electricians need to be able to understand and use symbols, graphs, tables and wiring diagrams. They must also be able to use measuring and mathematical skills when working with a range of equipment.
- Problem solving. This involves analysing the tasks to be undertaken and deciding on the most efficient and appropriate way to complete them. You will also need to review and evaluate outcomes in order to learn from experience.
- Working with others. You need to be able to work with colleagues and others to agree team goals and take responsibility for your own work.

You also need to have suitable qualifications. But we'll have a look at that aspect in the next chapter.

WHAT TOOLS DO YOU USE?

An electrician uses a number of different tools in his or her work. Look at the following tasks and decide which tools you would need to use to do the job from the list that follows.

1. Checking the correct operation of an RCD (residual current device) and measuring the insulation resistance of circuit cabling.

2. Checking that the electricity supply is dead before the work begins.

3. Stripping cables and wires, and connecting components and accessories.

4. Cutting small nuts, bolts and cables.

5. Smoothing the sharp edges on a steel conduit, cable tray and trunking.

6. Tightening metal sockets and couplings into the conduit.

7. Lifting up floorboards and chasing grooves down walls for burying cables.

8. Lifting up floorboards.

9. Cutting steel conduit and trunking.

10. Cutting wood, including floorboards.

A Files
B Flooring bolster
C Grips
D Junior hacksaw
E Large hacksaw
F Screwdrivers and pliers
G Test lamp
H Test meter
I Tenon saw
J Claw hammer

Answers on page 34

DRESSED TO IMPRESS

You can often spot electricians by the clothing and apparatus they wear. Those working in contracting and power distribution are likely to have the following as part of their wardrobe:

- hard hat – made from heavy duty plastic
- goggles – to protect the eyes
- face mask – for use in very dusty conditions
- overalls – a boiler suit, bib and braces or warehouse coat
- boots – with steel toecaps
- earplugs – to use when working with noisy drills, etc.
- gloves – to protect hands from blisters, splinters and corrosive substances
- knee pads – to use when kneeling for long periods.

Protective clothing is also worn in factories.

Answers:

1. H

2. G

3. F

4. D

5. A

6. C

7. B

8. J

9. E

10. I

What qualifications do I need?

Who needs qualifications? Nowadays most people do. Would you travel on an aircraft if you heard that the pilot didn't have a licence? Or undergo an operation if you knew the surgeon hadn't spent a day in medical school? Of course you wouldn't. In the same way, people want to have evidence that the electrician who wires their house or repairs their household appliances has been properly trained.

Being an electrician is a skilled job, and when you apply for jobs, employers will want to know what you know and what experience you have. To simplify matters for them, there is a system of nationally recognised qualifications that are approved by organisations representing different industrial sectors. These were formerly known as Training Councils but are now evolving into Sector Skills Councils. Not all sectors of the electrical and electronics sector have Skills Councils yet.

This section gives you an idea of the different subjects you can get qualifications in and what the qualifications actually stand for. You don't need to read through the whole of this section at this stage, but you may find it useful to refer to it later.

WHAT ARE NVQS AND SVQS?

National Vocational Qualifications (in England, Wales and Northern Ireland) and Scottish Vocational Qualifications assess the skills and abilities needed at work. Assessments are usually conducted at the workplace (or at work and college) with your manager or supervisor acting as your assessor. The qualifications are made up of a number of core and optional units, and trainees choose the most suitable combination of units for them. Apprentices normally work towards NVQs/SVQs as part of their training.

There are five levels: Level 1, Level 2, Level 3, Level 4 and Level 5.

- Level 1 indicates you can tackle basic or unskilled work.
- Level 2 means you are semi-skilled and have a broad range of skills and abilities.
- Level 3 shows you can do complex, technical, skilled work and can supervise others.
- Level 4 marks you out as a manager or specialist.
- Level 5 means you can progress to senior managerial level.

If you reach Level 2 you will be in position to get a job. If you reach Level 3 you will be regarded as a fully qualified electrician/technician. To reach the next levels you need to go on to higher education to study for a Higher National Diploma (HND) or a degree.

WHAT KIND OF SUBJECTS CAN I GET THESE QUALIFICATIONS IN?

Here are some examples of NVQ qualifications awarded by City & Guilds:

- Level 2 and 3 NVQ in Electricity Supply, Power Generation and Distribution (2353)
- Level 2 NVQ in Installing Electrotechnical Systems (2356)
- Level 3 NVQ in Electrotechnical Services (2356)
- Level 3 NVQ in Electrical Panel Building (2356)
- Level 3 NVQ in Electrical Machine Repair and Rewind (2356)
- Level 3 NVQ in Electrotechnical Services (2356). Four options: Electrical Installation (Buildings and Structures); Electrical Maintenance; Installing Instrumentation and Associated Equipment; Installing Public Lighting and Associated Equipment
- Level 2 and 3 NVQ in Electrical and Electronic Servicing (2248)

WHICH ARE THE MAIN AWARDING BODIES?

City & Guilds – or, to give it its full title, the City & Guilds of London Institute – is a registered charity established to provide education and training. It is the leading vocational award-making body in the UK and offers 500 qualifications at all levels. All the NVQs listed above are awarded by City & Guilds.

The main awarding body in Scotland is the Scottish Qualifications Authority (SQA). In Wales, it is the Qualifications, Curriculum and Assessment Authority for Wales (ACCAC) – see Resources for contact details.

Edexcel also offers NVQs, though not in electrical and electronics skills. It is best known for its First Diplomas, National Diplomas/Certificates, and Higher National Diplomas/Certificates which are awarded in subjects such as

- Electronics (First Diploma only)
- Electrical/Electronic Engineering
- Electronic Engineering
- Electrical Engineering
- Operations and Maintenance.

These are sometimes known as BTEC diplomas and certificates. In Scotland these awards are called Scottish National Diplomas, etc. Edexcel also offers Vocational A-levels in Engineering (VCEs). These are three-, six- or 12-unit qualifications, which include optional units in Electronics and Electrical and Electronic Principles.

EMTA Awards Ltd, part of SEMTA (the Science, Engineering and Manufacturing Technologies Alliance), also offers awards, notably:

- NVQ Levels 2 and 3 in Electrical and Electronic Servicing
- Foundation Certificate in Electronics.

WHAT OTHER AWARDS CAN I STUDY FOR?

ACHIEVEMENT MEASUREMENT 2 (AM2)/FINAL INTEGRATED COMPETENCE ASSESSMENT (FICA) (in Scotland)

This is the final test of the electrical apprenticeship. It is a test of practical skills, takes three days to complete and is conducted at one of a limited number of specially designated centres.

PROGRESSION AWARDS

These are awarded on the basis of assignments and written tests and can be studied at college, training centres or by correspondence.

Examples are:

- Automotive Servicing and Repair (auto-electrical) Levels 1–3 (4100)
- Electrical and Electronic Servicing Levels 2–3 (6958).

AWARDS FOR PRACTISING ELECTRICIANS
Examples are:

- Certificate in the Requirements for Electrical Installation BS7671: Level 3 Certificate (2381)
- Certificate in the Code of Practice for In-service Inspection and Testing of Electrical Equipment Level 3 (2377)
- Certificate in Inspection, Testing and Certification of Electrical Installations Level 3 (2391).

Practising electricians who have experience but have no certificates to show that they have can gain NVQ/SVQ certification under the Crediting Electrotechnical Competence (CEC) scheme by taking a practical test.

OTHER VOCATIONAL AWARDS
Assessment of other vocatoional awards is usually by a written paper and a practical test. Examples are:

- Certificate in Electrical Installation: Levels 2 and 3 (2330)
- Certificate in Electrical Technology Engineering: Level 3 (2322)
- Certificate in Electrical Installation: Levels 2 and 3 (2360)
- Entertainment and Theatre Electricians Award: Levels 1 and 2 (1810).

WHAT ARE KEY/CORE SKILLS?

Key Skills (Core Skills in Scotland) are qualifications that will boost your employability, whatever job you apply for. They form part of an apprenticeship and can help you gain valuable points if you plan to go on to higher education. The skills fall into six categories:

- communication
- application of number
- information technology
- working with others
- improving one's own learning
- problem solving.

Just in case you are getting confused, here is a diagram which shows how these different qualifications fit into the grand scheme of things.

progression chart
FOR ELECTRICIANS

ENTRY/PRE-ENTRY LEVEL	LEVEL 1	LEVEL 2	LEVEL 3
NO FORMAL QUALIFICATIONS REQUIRED	NO FORMAL QUALIFICATIONS REQUIRED	2-4 GCSEs (C-E grade) FOUNDATION GNVQ NVQ LEVEL 1	4-5 GCSEs (A-C grade) INTERMEDIATE GNVQ NVQ LEVEL 2

| GATEWAY TO EDUCATION AND TRAINING | ACCESS TO EMPLOYMENT LEVEL 1 AWARD NVQ LEVEL 1 KEY SKILLS LEVEL 1 | BTEC FIRST DIPLOMA GNVQ INTERMEDIATE GCSE PROGRAMME FOUNDATION 2 APPRENTICESHIP NVQ LEVEL 2 KEY SKILLS LEVEL 2 | BTEC NATIONAL CERTIFICATE BTEC NATIONAL DIPLOMA A/AS LEVELS VCE (Vocational A-Levels) ADVANCED 2 APPRENTICESHIP NVQ LEVEL 3 DIPLOMA IN 6TH FORM STUDIES |

EMPLOYMENT

EMPLOYMENT OR HIGHER EDUCATION

5

THE APPRENTICES

Case studies

ELECTRONIC ENGINEERING TECHNICIAN

Leon Newman works for a specialist manufacturing company that makes wipers for large cargo ships. Unlike car windscreen wipers these do not pivot, but slide across the windows and have more powerful motors. Leon is currently studying for a BTEC National Certificate in Electronic Engineering.

'I work with six others making the electronic units for the wipers,' he explains. 'I wire together the components and then try them out using testing equipment which simulates the ship. Wipers come in different sizes and colours and have varied functions. The ship operators specify their needs and we match their requirements, such as heated windows and the operating speed. The ships' engineers install the windows but we may have to go out to repair them.'

Leon joined the firm three years ago, and after he had been there two years was offered a full apprenticeship. At first he was wary. 'I'm a very practical person, but I struggle with the theory,' he says. However, he admits that the theoretical

I wanted to get a recognised qualification so I would have better prospects if decided to move on.

knowledge he has learned on the course so far has proved very useful in his work.

RADIO AND TV SERVICING TECHNICIAN

Ben Pillinger works for an independent radio and TV retailer who also has a repair facility. Ben did his work experience with the company while he was still at school and worked part-time for them at weekends. When he left school he was offered a job with the firm and decided to take it.

He has finished his apprenticeship (formerly called a Foundation Modern Apprenticeship) and is now working towards a City & Guilds Level 3 Certificate. He is also doing a BTEC National Certificate in Electronics.

'I wanted to get a recognised qualification so I would have better prospects if I decided to move on,' he says. 'The job varies quite a lot, and lately I have been going out in a van to service or install sets in people's homes. Most of the faults tend to occur in TVs, which sometimes develop dry joints that need soldering. There are seven or eight of us working for the company and we attend to the jobs as they come in.'

In addition to repairing radios and TVs, Ben also repairs DVD players and video recorders.

ELECTRONICS APPRENTICE

Having gained 11 GCSEs, James Purveur was taken on as an apprentice by a leading aerospace company. He is currently in the first year of a three-year apprenticeship and is studying for a BTEC National Certificate in Electronics and NVQs Level 2 and 3.

During his first year he has undergone full-time training at a training centre (for the practical component of the course) and his local further education college (for the theory). During the next two years he will be getting practical experience on the shop floor and attending college one day a week.

When he has not been training, he has worked for short periods in the company as a customer service workshop technician. 'This has involved me shadowing other workshop technicians,' he explains. 'One particular job I did was to test altimeters for tolerances. If there was a problem with them I had to take them apart, look inside and rectify them, where possible.'

During the next two years he will be getting practical experience on the shop floor and attending college one day a week.

ELECTRONICS TECHNICIAN

John Sowler passed AS level in Electronics and joined a company that designs and makes printed circuit boards for fruit machines and white goods (e.g. refrigerators, washing machines). He is currently in his first year of a trainee scheme and is studying for a Higher National Certificate in Electronics.

The boards that John works on are fairly standard designs and the work involves drawing the components from the stores and soldering them on to Veroboard. These boards are usually simple prototypes of simple products, but his company also does work on much more complex designs. The finished boards are then sent to the firm's customers to install in their products.

John is pleased because the company allows him to do as much training as he likes. He plans to stay with the firm for another year but is keeping his options open. One possibility he is considering is to take a degree course.

SIGNALLING APPRENTICE
Tom Croose is in the second year of an apprenticeship with Network Rail and hopes to be a fully qualified signalling technician two years from now.

Technicians work in teams of three or four, maintaining either the cables or the points. As part of his practical experience Tom has worked in both kinds of team.

The cable team tests the cables between the signal box and the signals and replaces or repairs any that are defective. Most signals on Britain's railways are electrically operated, but Tom notes that there are still parts of the network where signals continue to be operated mechanically.

The points team repairs faults to points. These have electrical detection circuits, which alert the signal box to any defects. The team ensures that the electric motors of the points are working properly and replaces them if they are not.

'In this job we use testing equipment and a lot of different tools,' says Tom. 'The main ones are screwdrivers, crimpers for wiring, and box spanners. Safety is very important and formed an important part of the NVQ2. This is very much an open-air job, which is fine during the summer, but not so nice in winter.'

Technicians work in teams of three or four, maintaining either the cables or the points. As part of his practical experience Tom has worked in both kinds of team.

RELIABILITY ENGINEER

Now aged 29, Philip Trewin is a mature trainee who was originally assigned by an outside consultancy to his present firm to do flow charting consulting. He was then offered permanent employment with the firm and later took an internal transfer to his present job. He learned his skills on the job, but as he needs to have a relevant qualification he is currently studying for a BTEC National Certificate in Electronic Engineering.

He works in the avionics division of a major aerospace company. 'There's a lot of predictive work in avionics where we see if we can meet our customers' requirements. The specification will ask for a reliability figure and we look at the amount of work involved and the cost to see if the project is realistic before we bid for it. We run models to see if they come up to specification and then check to see what, if any, improvements need to be made. We try to identify major problems that could be caused by such things as excessive vibration or extremes of temperature.'

The work has its advantages and disadvantages. 'Some of the jobs are very routine, but there are others that are much more challenging and interesting. Some involve investigation or interaction with the customer. I'm happy with the job and hope to combine the skills I develop from my course with the practical experience I have gained.'

Training day

6

You have seen the kind of qualifications necessary to become an electrician or electronics technician. How do you set about getting them? Does it involve more full-time study or can you obtain them while you are doing the job? In fact, either route is possible. The one you choose will be dependent partly on your circumstances and requirements and partly on what is available in your local area.

A young person, for instance, may need to start from the very beginning, whereas an older person may already have some technical qualifications and just need to top up or update his or her knowledge. Others may have plenty of experience but need to get some qualifications in order to move on to a better job. If you are uncertain which way to go, you should seek advice.

If you are still at school or have recently left, your school careers adviser or the local Connexions office should be able to give you an idea of local training opportunities available, including apprenticeships. Your local Learning and Skills Council (LSC), FE college or relevant Sector Skills Council or Training Council are other good sources of advice, especially for older entrants. (You should note that there is as yet no properly structured entry route into electrical/electronic manufacturing, although individual companies have their own training schemes.)

If you live in Scotland you should contact the Scottish Electrical Charitable Training Trust; residents of Northern

Ireland are recommended to get in touch with the Electrical
Training Trust. (Contact details are given in the Resources
section of this book.)

Those who are planning to join the armed forces should
enquire about apprenticeships and other training
opportunities in various electrical trades. The Royal
Engineers, Royal Electrical and Mechanical Engineers, the
Royal Corps of Signals, the Royal Navy, the RAF and other
branches of the armed forces offer training leading to
nationally recognised qualifications (NVQ/SVQ, City & Guilds,
Edexcel), which can prove invaluable if you eventually decide
to re-enter civilian life.

COLLEGE-BASED TRAINING

All over the country there are further education colleges
(sometimes called technical colleges) and other training
centres that offer full-time courses leading to Edexcel
Foundation Engineering Awards and National Diplomas.
They also offer part-time courses (e.g. day-release courses),
which often form an important component in apprenticeships
or other work-based training. The best ones have been
designated Centres of Vocational Excellence (CoVEs) by the
Learning and Skills Council.

College-based training is definitely not all chalk and talk. In
many centres the traditional blackboard has been replaced
by electronic boards and screens, which makes
understanding much easier. Textbooks are much livelier and
clearer than they were in the past and there are now a
number of interactive courses available on CD-ROM or on-
line. Even examinations can now be completed via the
Internet.

WORK-BASED TRAINING

A number of firms offer various types of on-the-job training leading to nationally recognised vocational qualifications (NVQs and SVQs). Apprenticeships, in particular, are highly regarded and if you complete one, successfully gaining an S/NVQ Level 3 or other qualifications, then your career has got off to a very promising start. However, nobody should regard apprenticeships as a pushover. If you have insufficient motivation you may not stay the course.

Let's look at apprenticeships in greater detail, particularly the more advanced type of apprenticeship. Do you have any idea of what an apprenticeship is like? The following questions are designed to find out.

1. What does an apprentice do on an employer's site?
   a) You are part of a team that turns up and does a day's work.
   b) Getting experience is really important; passing exams does not count for much.
   c) No-one pays much attention to apprentices, so they can do what they want.
   d) Apprentices do not take any responsibility because they are still learning.

2. How important is the experience you get on site?
   a) New apprentices don't learn much because they mostly tidy up and run errands.
   b) You are thrown in at the deep end as there are never enough qualified people to do the work.
   c) The experience on-site is important but initially it may seem dull. You only get jobs if you can work on them safely.

    d) You get hands-on experience from the word go. The theory you need is learnt through practical work.

3. Would you be working towards a career with real prospects?
    a) Yes. In terms of pay and opportunities the sky's the limit for people with electrical skills.
    b) With a qualification as an electrician you are limited to fairly trivial work.
    c) As a qualified electrician you need to know the right people to get work.
    d) Being an electrician means having a good steady job but no real prospects of promotion.

4. Is attending college or a training centre really necessary?
    a) If you can read and write, add up and use your hands, you will find college work easy.
    b) College work is boring and has nothing to do with real work.
    c) Going to college means more exams, but they are not as important as good practical work.
    d) College work is demanding, but you have to take the tests if you want to qualify.

5. How do you think employers regard advanced apprentices?
    a) Apprentices move from employer to employer for short-term jobs to gain the full range of experience.
    b) Most employers are not interested in taking on apprentices.
    c) Employers invest a lot of time and money in apprentices and expect them to stay with them.
    d) If you work with an employer during your training you have to stay with them for two years after you qualify.

6. What happens to your pay?
   a) Your pay is really pocket money as all your expenses are paid for you.
   b) Your family has to be prepared to look after you because your pay will not be enough to live on when you begin.
   c) You pay some of your expenses but your college and exam fees are paid for you by your employer.
   d) From the start of your apprenticeship you do real work and get paid a good wage.

Now look at the following table and work out your score.

Question	A	B	C	D
1	4	3	1	2
2	1	1	4	3
3	4	3	1	2
4	2	0	3	4
5	1	1	4	0
6	1	2	4	3

How did you get on?

If you scored 21–24 you clearly have a good idea of what an apprenticeship is all about.

If you scored 16–20 you have some idea but need to find out more about electrical apprenticeships.

If you scored under 15 you obviously have only a hazy idea. Read on and find out more.

WHY DO AN APPRENTICESHIP?

There are a number of advantages to doing an apprenticeship. In particular:

- a clear structure for entry into the chosen sector
- a short induction programme designed to introduce trainees to the world of work. It will normally include: an introduction to health and safety matters; basic electrical/electronic competencies; an introduction to both the industry and the company; an outline of the training programme; and an analysis of any additional training needed.
- training in four Key Skills areas: communication; application of number; information technology; and personal skills (either working with others or improving one's own performance)
- training in the safe use of tools and equipment
- an appropriate vocational education qualification (optional)
- flexibility to progress to a job-specific NVQ2 or 3 (SVQ3 in Scotland).
- the possibility of full-time employment or at least a work placement.

> **DID YOU KNOW?**
>
> A typical Apprenticeship offers: Initial Engineering Training plus Electrical/Electronics Engineering Skills at NVQ Level 2 or 3 plus A college course (e.g. one year of a City & Guilds course) plus Key/Core Skills

REGIONAL VARIATIONS

The apprenticeship system varies according to where you live in the United Kingdom and is liable to change.

England
The apprenticeship system in England was revamped in 2004 and now has a four-stage structure. It is possible to start at any stage depending on your experience and qualifications.

- Young Apprenticeships are for 14–16-year-olds. They involve up to two days a week outside the classroom learning a trade in a workshop.
- Pre-apprenticeships (Entry to Employment – E2E) are intended for young people who have potential but are not yet ready to do an apprenticeship. They lead to NVQ Level 1.
- Apprenticeships used to be called Foundation Modern Apprenticeships. They lead to an NVQ Level 2 award. It is possible to get a job once you have completed this apprenticeship successfully.
- Advanced Apprenticeships used to be called Advanced Modern Apprenticeships. They are open to people of all ages, not just to school leavers. They lead to NVQ Level 3 and qualified electrician status.

Wales
There are two types of apprenticeship available in Wales.

- Foundation Modern Apprenticeships leading to NVQ Level 2.
- Advanced Modern Apprenticeships leading to NVQ Level 3 and qualified electrician status.

In addition, there is a scheme entitled Skillbuild, which is designed to give 16–17-year-olds essential skills and build their confidence before they go on to an apprenticeship. This is similar to the Pre-apprenticeship in England.

Northern Ireland
The Apprenticeship scheme is equivalent to the Advanced Apprenticeship in England and leads to NVQ Level 3 and qualified electrician status.

Scotland
Skillseekers Modern Apprenticeships lead to an SVQ Level 3 and qualified electrician status.

APPRENTICESHIPS: QUESTIONS AND ANSWERS
What are the age limits for apprenticeships?
Apart from Young Apprenticeships, which are quite new, the starting age tends to be between 16 and 19, though some firms have been prepared to take on people outside this age range. From now on – in England, at least – firms will be able to accept applicants of all ages.

What qualifications do I need?
To be accepted for an Advanced Apprenticeship (or Modern Apprenticeship in Scotland and Ireland), you should have at least GCSE Grade C or above in English, Maths and a science subject. (The Scottish equivalent to GCSE is Standard Grade.) The better your qualifications and the more you have, the better your chances of getting the apprenticeship of your choice. Be warned. Competition to become an apprentice can be very keen.

What if I don't have these grades?
Some firms will accept you if your grades are lower than this or even if you have no qualifications, provided you pass an aptitude test. (Mature would-be trainees may well be

accepted on the strength of their performance in the aptitude test alone.) In England and Wales you can do an Apprenticeship (or Foundation Apprenticeship) for which lower grades are required. England has recently introduced Pre-apprenticeship training for those who are not quite ready for the full programme.

How long does it take to complete an apprenticeship?
The completion time for an Advanced Apprenticeship (Skillseekers/Modern Apprenticeship in Scotland, Apprenticeship in Northern Ireland) varies according to age. For apprentices aged 16–18 it is normally three to four years. Those aged 19 and over may be able to complete their apprenticeship sooner. Other forms of apprenticeship tend to be shorter. However, bear in mind that doing an apprenticeship is not a soft option and there is a considerable drop-out rate.

What qualifications will I get?
This will depend on which apprenticeship scheme you go for. If you are doing an Advanced Apprenticeship in electrical contracting, for instance, you should end up with

- S/NVQ (Level 3) in Installing and Commissioning Electrotechnical Systems
- Achievement Measurement 2 (AM2)/Final Integrated Competence Assessment (FICA)
- Practical Test qualification
- Key/Core Skills qualification.

How much time is spent studying at college?
Normally one day a week will be spent at a college or training centre. The rest of the time is spent getting practical experience on site.

action plan

DISCUSS YOUR CAREER OPTIONS WITH YOUR CAREERS OFFICER OR OTHER ADVISER

OBTAIN APPLICATION FORM FROM YOUR CAREERS OFFICER. COMPLETE AND SEND TO YOUR LOCAL LSC, SECTT (SCOTLAND), ETT (NORTHERN IRELAND)

ATTEND INDUSTRY PRE-EMPLOYMENT ASSESEMENT AT DATE AND TIME ARRANGED BY YOUR LOCAL LSC ETC.

FAIL TO ACHIEVE QUALIFYING STANDARD

ACHIEVE QUALIFYING STANDARD

APPLY TO LOCAL ELECTRICAL FIRMS FOR AN APPRENTICESHIP

ATTEND PROSPECTIVE EMPLOYER FOR AN INTERVIEW

NO OFFER OF AN APPRENTICESHIP

RECIEVE AN OFFER OF AN APPRENTICESHIP FROM AN EMPLOYER

ADVISE EMPLOYER OF YOUR ACCEPTANCE OF THE OFFER

What are the normal working hours?
On days when you are being trained you will usually work
between 9 am and 5 pm. If you are working on site you will
probably have to start much earlier and the length of the day
may vary.

Who pays?
For those aged 16–19 the cost of the training is met by the
local Learning and Skills Council (SECTT in Scotland; ETT in
Northern Ireland). Older people may be eligible for financial
help from these organisations, and funds may also be
available under the Government's New Deal scheme or from
the European Social Fund.

The better your qualifications and the more you
have, the better your chances of getting the
apprenticeship of your choice.

TRAINING AGREEMENTS

Before you begin an apprenticeship you will have to sign a Training Agreement with your employer and any training organisation that may be involved. A typical agreement will be along the following lines:

TRAINING AGREEMENT

This agreement between (trainee's name)

and (parent/guardian's name, if trainee is under 18)

and (company's name)

and (LSC's name*)

is made on (date).

1. The company's responsibilities in accordance with the apprenticeship agreement are:
   a) to employ and pay the trainee
   b) to undertake their legal and contractual responsibilities for the health and safety of the trainee
   c) to provide the trainee, as far as is reasonably practical, with the experience, facilities and training necessary to achieve the training objectives specified in the training plan
   d) to use reasonable endeavours, with the assistance of various local groups/networks, to

---

arrange employment elsewhere should the company be unable to provide employment after the completion of training.

2. The Trainee's (and, if applicable, the Parent/Guardian's) responsibilities in accordance with the traineeship agreement are for the trainee:
   a) to be employed and to work for the company
   b) to observe the company's terms and conditions of employment
   c) in both work and training, to be diligent and punctual and attend courses, keep records and take tests to be determined by the company in order to achieve the training plan objectives
   d) to behave in a responsible manner and in accordance with the requirements of Health and Safety legislation relating to the individual's responsibilities
   e) to promote the company's interests.

3. The LSC's responsibilities are:
   a) to confirm to the company and trainee (and, if applicable, parent/guardian) that the contents of the training plan fulfil the national and industry/sector criteria for Apprenticeships
   b) to monitor the training so that the training meets the LSC quality assurance process (TQASM) and the standards of the Training Standards Council, including health and safety obligations required of LSCs and their providers and the inspection requirements of government funded training.

c) to promise the trainee (and, if applicable, the parent/guardian) that if the company is unable to complete the traineeship, it shall use its best endeavours within three months to ensure that the trainee is offered the opportunity to transfer to another provider under the terms of the training plan substantially similar to the existing training plan

d) to confirm to the company and trainee that it will make the payments for the training as set out in the LSC provider agreement.

Signed (trainee's name)

(parent/guardian's name, if trainee is under 18)

(company's name)

(LSC's name)

* SECTT in Scotland; ETT in Northern Ireland

7

Career opportunities and prospects

Once you have finished your training and gained the qualifications you need, you will naturally want to find a good job in which you can use the skills you have learned and earn a living.

If you have been an apprentice you may be tempted to stay on with the firm that trained you, but you don't have to. Fortune often favours those who are prepared to move on and get a wide range of experience. So well before your training comes to an end you should keep an eye open for job opportunities.

You will find job advertisements in:

- national newspapers
- local newspapers
- trade and professional journals (see the Resources section in this book)
- Job Centres
- private recruitment agencies.

You could also surf the web. Try looking at the websites of

companies and organisations that employ electricians and electronics specialists, as well as other recruitment sites, such as:

- www.worktrain.gov.uk
- www.lgjobs.com (for jobs in local government)
- www.amicustheunion.org
- www.careers-scotland.org.uk (Scotland only)
- www.ceg.org.uk (Scotland only)
- www.jobcentreplus.gov.uk

Don't be hesitant to use your contacts. Your college instructor may know of suitable jobs on offer in your locality and so may your local Learning and Skills Council (Local Enterprise Company in Scotland). A number of the trade organisations listed in the reference section operate a recruitment service for their members – as does Amicus-AEEU.

Even if they don't, you will be able to get a list of their member companies from their websites. These companies in turn will have their own websites, which are almost bound to have a page devoted to vacancies. You could find jobs listed here that have not yet been advertised publicly.

SPECIMEN ADVERTISEMENTS

CRAFTSPERSON
Various Locations   Up to £21k

National Grid Transco is one of the world's most experienced and highly respected names in the operation of complex energy networks.

If you have served a modern apprenticeship in an electrical or mechanical discipline, including City and Guilds 232 or a relevant NVQ Level 3, with at least 18 months' practical experience, this is your opportunity to sharpen your skills and extend your experience in a world-class organisation. Working on our substations, you will gain experience across a wide range of duties on high-voltage plant and equipment, carrying out maintenance and basic fault-finding – working largely unsupervised either within a team or alone.

You will be an integral member of a mobile workforce travelling direct to sites, which means you must have a full driving licence and flexibility towards work and its completion. Good communication skills, plenty of initiative, high standards and strong motivation will also be essential.

FIELD SERVICE ENGINEER
Location: South Wales   £15k–16k pa

Applicant must be a non-smoker. Must be able to demonstrate fault-finding ability and the effective use of hardware and software test and diagnostic facilities. Must have proven ability to construct and maintain good relationships with customers and work colleagues and act as part of a team. Must have a total of at least 2 years' relevant experience. Duties include providing a fault-finding, repair and maintenance service on a limited range of projects. Will be responsible for identifying the cause of equipment breakdown, undertaking installation or enhancement of equipment and ensuring set standards regarding health and safety are complied with.

CHARGEHAND/ELECTRICIAN
Location: West Midlands   £350 p.w.

You must have Electrical City and Guilds Craft Certificates, have served a recognised apprenticeship, possess 16th Edition IEE Regulations Certificate and 2 years' craft experience. Experience is required in the fault finding, repair and maintenance of electrical engineering plant and services associated with hospital premises or other large buildings. Whilst undertaking the duties of the craftsperson you will also have the responsibility of leading and motivating a small team of maintenance electricians and assistants. This will include issuing work dockets and monitoring overall team performance.

CAREER DEVELOPMENT

As you gain in experience you may well find yourself taking on a supervisory role, in which you have to manage not only yourself but a team of craftsmen/technicians. Being a supervisor, team leader or foreman entails using more than just your practical skills. You will need to communicate clearly and have leadership qualities which will enable you to get a job finished on time.

In some areas you may move into roles which are less hands-on, such as working in the design or development office, working as an estimator, liaising with clients and managing contracts.

Larger organisations usually have a clearly defined career ladder. Here is how you might progress if you were working as an electrician for a railway company:

Electrician ⇨ Assistant Technician ⇨ Technician ⇨ Senior Technician ⇨ Assistant Electrification Engineer ⇨ Professional Head of Electrification Engineering ⇨ Senior Management

Smaller firms will have a less hierarchical structure and you may find yourself taking on responsibilities quite quickly. You might eventually decide to follow the example of Tony Morgan in Chapter 1 and opt to become self-employed – especially common in the contracting and servicing sector.

THE REWARDS

It is difficult to predict exactly how large your pay packet will be once you are suitably qualified. The type of job you are doing, your qualifications and experience, the geographical location and the size of the company you are working for can all affect your pay. The organisation Incomes Data Services publishes a survey of benchmark incomes three times a year, and for up-to-date information you should consult that. As a general rule, the income range starts at £13,000 a year and can rise to £30,000 and beyond.

Here are some recent examples from Incomes Data Services:

- Electrician in the vehicle building industry: £234 per week
- NHS Maintenance Electrician: £331 per week
- BBC Electrician: £15,198–£24,048 per year (£18,565–£27,064 in London)
- Network Rail: £24,602–£31,498
- Electrical Maintenance Engineer (Thorn): £19,294
- Electrician (BAE Systems): £20,950.

Here are some more examples seen recently on the Worktrain jobs website:

- Radiotherapy Equipment Maintenance Technician (Yorkshire): £12,321–£15,362
- Field Service Engineer (Cardiff): £15,000–£16,000
- Maintenance Electrician (Shetland): £17,768
- Maintenance Electrician (Birmingham): £20,565
- Security Service Engineer (London): £21,000–£30,000
- Electrical Installation Test Engineers: £9–£10 per hour
- Maintenance Electrician (Herts): £12.50 per hour

In the electrical contracting industry you could have expected to earn the following hourly rates for a 37.5 hour week at the beginning of 2004:

- Electrician: £8.25 (£9.10 in London)
- Approved Electrician: £9.05 (£9.91 in London)
- Technician: £10.34 (£11.23 in London)

On top of that you get extra if you're using your own transport to get to the site, a travelling time payment and overtime. When working away from home you will be paid a subsistence allowance.

Recently qualified electricians in this industry can normally expect to earn an annual wage of £20,000 – and often considerably more.

However, you may find that the rewards amount to much more than just your pay packet. You gain respect from others and satisfaction when you have done a job well.

FORGING AHEAD

If you are really serious about getting on, one very good way is to become a fully fledged engineer. This will inevitably involve further study – for a Higher National Certificate or a Foundation degree, for example. The range of electrical and electronics engineering degrees on offer is staggering. Here is just a sample:

- Electronic Design Engineering
- Microelectronics
- Electronic Systems
- Electrical Engineering
- Electromechanical Engineering.

Studying for an engineering degree needn't cost you a penny. The reason? Many engineering firms offer sponsorship to students who show promise, and if you've already proved your worth at the technician level you stand a good chance of getting funding. Your own firm may be willing to sponsor you; there's no harm in asking. You could also turn to a relevant professional institute – the Institution of Electrical Engineers or the Institution of Incorporated Engineers – for advice on sponsorship and how to progress in your career.

Once you have the title Chartered Engineer or Incorporated Engineer the world is your oyster. British electrical and electronics engineers are in demand all over the world.

Countless people who started off as electricians and electronics technicians have worked their way up to become contracts managers, project managers, systems designers, training officers and instructors, technical directors of major companies – even managing directors. Success did not come overnight, though. They worked hard and they studied hard. There is nothing that cannot be achieved if you put your mind to it.

Note: the salaries quoted in this chapter were current as this book went to press, but are liable to change.

The last word

By now you should have gained some idea of the range of jobs you could tackle within the electrical/electronics sector. The great thing about them is that they are in no sense dead-end jobs but offer opportunities to earn good money and progress to positions of responsibility – given sufficient motivation and ability on your part, of course.

It is now decision time for you. What do you think? Could you make a success of the job? Do you think you would enjoy it? Would you get sufficient job satisfaction from it? If you are still unsure, the next few pages list some useful contacts that can put you more clearly in the picture.

To help you make up your mind just have a look at this final checklist. Which of the following words and phrases describe you?

- keen to learn
- accurate and methodical
- safety conscious
- computer literate
- flexible
- good at working with your hands
- technically minded
- willing to take responsibility
- numerate

- able to follow diagrams
- good at communicating
- fond of problem solving.

If you have ticked all 12, congratulations! This is an excellent start. You appear to have all that it takes to be successful in this key profession.

Resources

Amicus-AEEU

Hayes Court, West Common Road, Hayes, Bromley, Kent
BR2 7AU
Tel: 020 7703 4231. Website: www.amicustheunion.org

The trade union for electricians. A partner in the Joint
Industry Board for the electrotechnical industry. Has a jobs
board on its website.

Arts and Entertainment Technical Training Initiative

14 Blenheim Terrace, London NW8 0EB
Tel: 020 7328 6174

Provides training for electricians in the entertainment
industry.

Association of Electricity Producers

1st Floor, 17 Waterloo Place, London SW1Y 4AR
Tel: 020 7930 9390. Website: www.aepuk.com

The trade association of the firms that produce electricity.

British Electrotechnical and Allied Manufacturers' Association (BEAMA)

3 Albert Embankment, London SE1 7SL
Tel: 020 7793 3000. Website: www.beama.org.uk

The trade association of manufacturers of electrical and
electronic equipment and appliances.

Careers and Occupational Information Unit
61 Fountain Street, Belfast BT1 5EX
Tel: 02890 441921. Website: www.delni.gov.uk

The Northern Ireland careers advice service.

Careers Scotland
Website: www.careers-scotland.org.uk

See Scottish Enterprise.

Centre for Rail Studies
Paddington Station, PO Box 39685, London W2 1XR
Tel: 0845 345 2700. Website: www.cfrs.org.uk

The training organisation for the railway industry.

City & Guilds
1 Giltspur Street, London EC1A 9DD
Tel: 020 7294 2468. Email: enquiry@city-and-guilds.co.uk
Website: www.city-and-guilds.co.uk

City & Guilds is the leading provider of vocational
qualifications in the UK. These include NVQs.

Connexions
Tel: 080 8001 3219. Websites: www.connexions.gov.uk;
www.connexions-direct.com.

Part of the DfES providing advice on jobs and training for
young people up to the age of 19.

Continuing Education Gateway
199 Nithsdale Road, Glasgow G41 5EX
Tel: 0800 442222. Website www.ceg.org.uk

Information service on the labour market, careers and
learning opportunities in Scotland.

Department for Education and Skills (DfES)
Sanctuary Buildings, Great Smith Street, London SW1P 3BT;
Moorfoot, Sheffield S1 4PQ
Website: www.dfes.gov.uk

Supports and provides information on training and education
in England.

Edexcel
Stuart House, 32 Russell Square, London WC1B 54DN
Tel: 0870 240 9800. Website: www.edexcel.org.uk

An examining body that offers diplomas and certificates in
electrical engineering and electronics.

Education and Learning Wales (ELWa)
Website: www.elwa.ac.uk

The National Council for Education and Training in Wales,
which plans and promotes further education, work-based
training, continuing education and education for the 16–19
age group.

Electrical Contractors' Association (ECA)
ESCA House, 34 Palace Court, London W2 4HY
Tel: 020 7313 4800. Website: www.eca.co.uk

A trade association representing companies involved in electrical installation. It provides a focus for the electrical industry in terms of safety, training, qualifications, technological development and industry performance.

Electrical and Electronics Servicing Training Council (EESTC)

c/o Electronics Examination Board (EEB), Savoy Hill House, Savoy Hill, London WC2R 0BS
Tel: 020 7395 0276. Email: eeb@iie.org.uk
Websites: www.eestc.co.uk; www.the-eeb.co.uk

The training council which sets standards for the electrical and electronics servicing industry. The EEB assesses practical skills in conjunction with City & Guilds.

Electrical Training Trust (ETT)

Ballymena Business Centre, Fernaghy Road, Ballymena, Co Antrim BT42 1FL
Tel: 02825 650750. Email: info@ett-ni.org.
Website: www.ett-ni.org

An organisation providing guidance and support for anyone in Ulster planning to train as an electrician.

EMTA Awards Ltd

Semta House, 14 Upton Road, Watford WD18 0JT
Tel: 01923 652400. Website: www.eal.org.uk

An examining body which offers vocational awards and NVQs in a variety of subjects.

Energy Networks Association
18 Stanhope Place, Marble Arch, London W2 2HA
Tel: 020 7706 5100. Website: www.energynetworks.org

The trade association of the electricity and gas transmission and distribution licence holders.

Energy & Utility Skills
Business Centre, Edward Street, Redditch B97 6HA
Tel: 01527 584848. Website: www.euskills.co.uk

The Sector Skills Council for electricity, gas, waste management and water. This sets training standards for the utilities industries.

Engineering Council
10 Maltravers Street, London WC2R 3ER
Tel: 020 7240 7891. Website: www.engc.org.uk

The body that sets standards for the training of engineers and acts as the central registration body for professional engineers and technicians.

E-Skills UK
1 Castle Lane, London SW1E 6DR
Tel: 020 7963 8920. Website: www.e-skills.com

The Sector Skills Council for the IT and telecommunications industry.

GAMBICA Association Ltd
St George's House, 195–203 Waterloo Road, London SE1 8WB
Tel: 020 7642 8080. Website: www.gambica.org.uk

The trade association for instrumentation, control automation and laboratory technology (including test and measurement equipment for the electronics and electrical industries).

Institution of Electrical Engineers
Michael Faraday House, Six Hills Way, Stevenage, Herts
SG1 2AY
Tel: 01438 313311. Website: www.iee.org.uk

The professional body for electrical engineers. Offers professional qualifications and advice on training and careers.

Institution of Incorporated Engineers
Savoy Hill House, Savoy Hill, London WC2R 0BS
Tel: 020 7836 3357. Website: www.iie.org.uk

A professional body providing education and training as well as a professional qualification for engineers and engineering technicians in electrical, electronic and mechanical engineering.

Intellect
Blackfriars House, 999 South Row, Milton Keynes MK9 2PQ
Tel: 01908 232200. Website: www.intellect-uk.com

The trade association of the IT, telecommunications and electronics industry.

Joint Industry Board for the Electrical Contracting Industry (JIB)
Kingswood House, 47–51 Sidcup Hill, Sidcup, Kent
DA14 6HP
Tel: 020 8302 0031

The joint organisation of employers (ECA) and the union (Amicus-AEEU) acting together to support the industry. It is responsible for the registration of apprentices in electrical contracting in the UK and works closely with JTL. Scotland has its own Joint Industry Board (SJIB), which is at the same address as the Scottish Electrical Charitable Training Trust.

JT Ltd (JTL)
Stafford House, 120/122 High Street, Orpington BR6 0JS
Tel: 01689 884100 or 0800 0852308. Website:
www.jtlimited.co.uk

A training provider owned by the electrotechnical (electrical contracting) industry. Arranges training and funding with colleges, training centres and other organisations in England and Wales.

learndirect
Dearing House, 1 Young Street, Sheffield S1 4UP
Tel: 0800 100900. Website: www.learndirect.co.uk

A service from the University of Industry providing advice on learning and training opportunities, some of them on-line.

Learning and Skills Council (LSC)
Charlesmire House, Quinton Road, Coventry CV1 2WT.
Tel: 0845 019 4170.
Websites: www.lsc.gov.uk; www.realworkrealplay.co.uk
(apprenticeship details).

A network of local organisations responsible for funding and planning education and training for those aged 16 and over in England and Wales. Your local LSC will be listed in the telephone directory. (In Scotland these are known as Local Enterprise Companies – LECs.)

Ministry of Defence
Websites: www.army.mod.uk/careers; www.rafcareers.com; www.royal-navy.mod.uk

The armed forces offer opportunities to train as an electrician or electronics technician – notably the Royal Navy, Royal Air Force, Royal Engineers, Royal Electrical and Mechanical Engineers and Royal Signals Corps. Your nearest Armed Services Career Information Office can also provide details.

Qualifications and Curriculum Authority
83 Piccadilly, London W1J 8QA
Tel: 020 7509 5555. Website: www.qca.org.uk

An independent body that maintains and develops the national curriculum and associated assessments, tests and examinations. It accredits and monitors qualifications.

Qualifications, Curriculum and Assessment Authority for Wales (ACCAC)
Castle Buildings, Womanby Street, Cardiff CF10 1SX
Tel: 029 2037 5400. Website: www.accac.org.uk

Science, Engineering and Manufacturing Technology Alliance (SEMTA)
14 Upton Road, Watford WD18 0JT
Tel: 0800 282167. Websites: www.semta.org.uk; www.enginuity.org.uk

Provides an engineering careers service and is the Sector Skills Council for Science, Engineering and Manufacturing.

Scottish Electrical Charitable Training Trust (SECTT)
Walled Garden, Bush Estate, Penicuik, Midlothian EH26 0SE
Tel: 0131 445 5659. Email: admin@sectt.org.uk.
Website: www.sectt.org.uk

An organisation providing advice, training or support for anyone planning to become an electrician in Scotland.

Scottish Electrical Contractors Association (SELECT)
Address as for SECTT
Tel: 0131 445 5577. Website: www.select.org.uk

The trade body for the electrical contracting industry in Scotland.

Scottish Enterprise
5 Atlantic Quay, 150 Broomielaw, Glasgow G2 8LU
Website: www.scottishenterprise.com

An official body that promotes employment and training through its 12 Local Enterprise Companies. In conjunction with Highlands and Islands Enterprise it operates the Careers Scotland website (www.careers-scotland.org.uk).

Scottish Qualifications Authority (SQA)
Hanover House, 24 Douglas Street, Glasgow G2 7NQ
Tel: 0845 279 1000. Website: www.sqa.org.uk

The Scottish equivalent of the Qualifications and Curriculum Authority.

Summit Skills
Fairbourne Drive, Atterbury, Milton Keynes MK10 9RG
Tel: 0800 0688336. Website: www.summitskills.org.uk

The Sector Skills Council for the building services
engineering sector (which includes electrical contracting). It
offers advice on training and careers.

Worktrain
Website: www.worktrain.gov.uk

A national database of job vacancies in different employment
sectors. Also offers careers advice and information about
study and training.

PUBLICATIONS

Electrical Review
Highbury House Communications, Media House, Azalea
Drive, Swanley, Kent BR8 8HU
Website: www.hhc.co.uk

Electrical Times
Address as for *Electrical Review*
Website: www.electricaltimes.co.uk

New Electronics
Findlay Publications Ltd, Franks Hall, Horton Kirby, Dartford
DA4 9LL
Tel: 01322 222222. Website: www.neon.co.uk